295.

Heroes
AND
Heroines

Eleanor and
Herbert Farjeon

DRAWINGS BY
ROBIN JACQUES

J. M. DENT & SONS LTD
London Melbourne

Text first published 1933. Copyright © Gervase Farjeon 1987
Illustrations © Robin Jacques 1987
All rights reserved

Phototypeset by Gee Graphics

Printed and bound in Great Britain by
Mackays of Chatham Ltd for
J.M. Dent & Sons Ltd
Aldine House, 33 Welbeck Street, London W1M 8LX

British Library Cataloguing in Publication Data

Farjeon, Eleanor
    Heroes and heroines. — New ed.
    1. Heroes — Juvenile poetry   2. Heroines   — Juvenile poetry
    I. Title   II. Farjeon, Herbert
    III. Jacques, Robin
    920'.02   CT107

ISBN 0-460-06262-X

Heroes and Heroines

Alexander the Great	4	Sir Philip Sidney	34
Julius Cæsar	6	Pocahontas	36
Boadicea	8	The Duke of	
Charlemagne	10	Marlborough	38
Alfred the Great	11	Rob Roy	39
Brian Boru	12	Flora Macdonald	40
Lady Godiva	14	George Washington	42
Hereward the Wake	16	Nelson	44
The Cid	17	Napoleon	46
Saladin	18	Wellington	48
Robert Bruce	20	Lady Hester Stanhope	50
Robin Hood	22	Garibaldi	52
William Tell	24	David Livingstone	54
Timon the Tartar	25	Grace Darling	56
Joan of Arc	26	Florence Nightingale	58
Christopher Columbus	28	Buffalo Bill	60
Mary Queen of Scots	30	Emmeline Pankhurst	62
Sir Francis Drake	32	Nansen	64

Alexander the Great

B.C. 356-323

*A*LEXANDER the Great,
　　Alexander the Great,
He conquered the world at a rollicking rate,
　　In a very few weeks
　　He defeated the Greeks
And scattered the Persians and settled their fate,
　　In a couple of twos
　　He walloped the Jews,
He skedaddled the Gypsies, unable to wait,
　　Then, cutting a dash,
　　He reduced in a flash
The Indian tribes to a similar state.

　　Alexander the Great
　　Looked very ornate
In his beautiful plumes and his gold armour-plate,
　　And he rode on a steed
　　Of the very best breed
With an elegant tail and a delicate gait,
　　But he sighed as he cried,
　　'I shall now have to ride
Home to Macedon since, I regret to relate,
　　With the map at my feet,
　　There is no one to beat,
I have conquered the world at too early a date!'

Julius Cæsar

B.C. 100-44

*J*ULIUS CÆSAR, pride of Rome,
Made the battlefield his home;
First he fought, and then he went
And wrote about it in his tent.

Cæsar conquered Rome and Gaul,
Belgium, Germany and all;
Then, with very little fuss,
He came and saw and conquered us.

When his battles he had won,
Cæsar, second unto none,
Always tried to civilize
And elevate his enemies.

Laws he taught them how to make,
Roads to lay, and bricks to bake;
Thus his foes, when they were beat,
Were benefited by defeat.

But the jealous Romans who
Saw how Cæsar's power grew
Whispered, 'Men who wax too great
Become a danger to the State.'

So they planned to shed his gore;
Even Marcus Brutus swore
In the Capitol to end
The life of Cæsar, his good friend.

One by one, they stabbed him through;
One by one, his blood they drew;
'Brutus! even thou!' he cried;
And Brutus struck; and Cæsar died.

Boadicea

1st Century A.D.

*B*OADICEA
Was frightened of no man
And scorned the idea
Of anything Roman,
(The Roman she hated
For treating the Briton
As something created
Expressly to sit on)
So when in her regions,
With fire and with pillage,
The conquering legions
Invaded each village,
This Queen of Iceni
Said, 'Say what you like, I
Am sick of their *veni*
And *vidi* and *vici* !'

Then urging her horses,
Her chariot lashing,
In front of her forces
Pugnaciously dashing,
With hair wildly streaming,
With wrath and rampaging,
With shouting and screaming
And stamping and raging,
With fearsome grimaces
And fury unshaken,
She took several places
The Romans had taken,
And left nothing undone
To make the foe go forth
From Colchester, London,
St. Albans and so forth.

But Roman Paulinus,
By no means enraptured
To hear he was minus
The towns he had captured,
Turned up and attacked her
With swiftness surprising,
And thoroughly whacked her
And put down the rising.
So Boadicea,
In failure resplendent,
Refusing to be a
Mere Roman dependent,
A poisonous fluid
Courageously swallowed.
Bemoaned by the Druid,
Her funeral followed.

Charlemagne
742-814

I SING my sweet King,
 Who rights all wrongs,
His deathless fame I sing
 In my poor songs.
  Charlemagne! Flower of France!
   Who would not die
  To win thy favouring glance?
   Fain would I!

I sing my King's sire,
 Pepin the Short,
The lord who gat a squire
 Of taller sort.
  Charlemagne! Crown of France!
   Who would not try
  To merit thy least glance?
   Fain would I!

I sing his fair dam,
 The Swanfoot Queen,
Who nurtured in her lamb
 The lion's mien.
  Charlemagne! Soul of France!
   Who would not sigh
  To earn thy pleasant glance?
   Fain would I!

I sing his Twelve Knights,
 His Paladins,
Who turned all wrongs to rights,
 And slew all sins.
  Charlemagne! Heart of France!
   Who would not cry
  The glory of thy glance?
   Fain would I!

I sing his bright blade,
 Joyous, his sword,
Which many a squire hath made
 Into a lord.
  Charlemagne! Sword of France!
   Who would not vie
  To gain thy welcome glance?
   Fain would I!

I sing the Oriflamme,
 The Flag of Gold,
In war the proudest claim
 For knight to hold.
  Charlemagne! Flame of France!
   Who would not buy
  With death thy lightest glance?
   Fain would I!

Alfred the Great
849-901

CHILL, shrill,
   wind bloweth,
up hill
Alfred goeth,
by Dane
down-trodden,
heart, brain,
skin sodden.

Rain raineth,
sludge sludgeth,
pain paineth,
Alfred trudgeth.

At hut
King knocketh,
old slut
unlocketh.
'Help, kind
crone, prithee!'
'Pack, hind!
Off with 'ee!'

Slut grumbleth,
Alfred prayeth,
slut mumbleth,
Alfred stayeth.

By glow
King stretcheth,
rye dough
slut fetcheth,
no whit
King heedeth
whiles it
slut kneadeth.

Heart warmeth,
Alfred lieth,
storm stormeth,
Alfred drieth.

'Watch bake
dough, fellow,
till cake
turn'th yellow,
whiles I
brave cruel
cold sky
fetching fuel.'

Glow gloweth,
gleam gleameth,
slut goeth,
Alfred dreameth.

In fire
future seeth:
King's ire
Dane fleeth,
King's arm
Dane feeleth,
flame's charm
heart healeth.

Alfred thinketh,
hope returneth,
fire winketh,
cake burneth.

Thwack! thwack!
slut clouteth!
'Cake's black!'
slut shouteth.

'Fool! dolt!'
King quaileth!
'Clod! colt!'
slut raileth.

Slut growleth,
rateth, ranteth,
screameth, scowleth,
prateth, panteth.

'Lout! block!
lackwit! looby!
stick! stock!
bull-head! booby!'
'Come, thing,'
Alfred sayeth,
'thy King
pardon prayeth!'

Slut moaneth,
weepeth, squealeth,
whineth, groaneth,
waileth, kneeleth.

'Up, slut!
wherefore grovel?
Sweet hut!
bless thy hovel!'
Birds trill,
cock croweth,
down hill
Alfred goeth.

Sky cleareth,
leaf drippeth,
sun cheereth,
Alfred skippeth.

Brian Boru

926-1014

*B*RIAN BORU, Boru, Boru,
Brian Boru, Boru!
Where did he live and what did he do,
And what was he like, aroo?
His face was fierce, and his beard was rough,
His eyes were big, and his voice was gruff,
His arms were mighty, his muscles were tough,
Brian Boru, Boru!

Brian Boru was a Munsterman,
His brother was King of the Munster Clan,
And when he died, quoth Brian Boru,
'I'll be King over Munster and Leinster too!'

Brian Boru with his army rude
The Kingdom of Leinster soon subdued,
But when he was King of Leinster, 'Pooh!
I'll be King of All Ireland!' said Brian Boru.

Brian Boru to Dublin sped,
He fought the Danes and their chief fell dead,
Then he put on the crown, and he cried 'Hooroo!'
And the Dubliners shouted for Brian Boru!

Ever since then the Irish race
Have adored Boru, in spite of his face,
And instead of boasting their blood is blue,
They declare, 'We're descended from Brian Boru!'

Brian Boru, Boru, Boru,
Brian Boru, Boru!
Though he stirred up a thoroughly Irish stew
Was no scholar at all, aroo!
In various ways he spelt his name,
So nobody spells it twice the same,
But he died in glory and lives in fame
As Brian Boru, Boru!

Lady Godiva

1040-1080

*L*ADY GODIVA,
Let your hair down!
Bare you must go
Through Coventry Town,
Riding your palfrey
Past window and door
Naked as Eve,
For love of the poor.

Lady Godiva
Pity implored
For the poor people
Oppressed by her lord.
'Pity, my lady!'
He sneered as he spake,
'What would *you* suffer
For pity's sweet sake?

'Lady Godiva,
Mount your white mare!
Ride along Coventry
Street if you dare
Stripped of your clothes
From your gown to your shift—
Do this, and pity
I'll grant as a gift!'

Lady Godiva
Through Coventry sent
Word that all windows
And doors should be pent;
She stripped off her shift,
And her hair she unbound,
It fell, a gold mantle,
Her body around.

Lady Godiva
Sat fair on her seat;
There wasn't a soul
To be seen in the street,
Or a sound to be heard
By the people inside
Save the clack on the cobbles
That told of her ride.

Lady Godiva,
Did none see at all?
A fellow named Tom
Made a hole in his wall;
He peeped as she passed,
All golden and white;
But heaven sent lightning
And stripped him of sight.

Lady Godiva
Rode naked to prove
That shame and injustice
Are weaker than love.
Cloaked in her hair
She rode back as she came;
Her lord kept his word
And her folk blessed her name.

Hereward the Wake
11th Century

*O*VER the marshy spaces,
   Over the salty grass,
Hereward skims and races—
Which of ye saw him pass?
Harrying William's forces,
Scourge of the Conqueror's men,
Winding his mazy courses,
Hereward's at it again!
Is it a wild swan screaming, screaming
         over the reedy land?
Or is it the cry of Hereward calling,
         calling his Saxon band?
Is it a bittern booming, booming,
         beating a lonely wing?
Or is it the laugh of Hereward mocking,
         mocking the Norman King?

Hereward hunting and hunted,
Hiding in swamp and bog,
Crouching by oak-stump stunted,
Couching beside the frog,
Hereward ever resisting,
Hereward fleet of heel,
Hereward turning, twisting,
Making the Norman reel!
Is it a grey goose flying, flying
         over the windy waste?
Or is the cloak of Hereward flitting,
         flitting in silent haste?
The wild swan screams, the bittern booms,
         the grey goose flies the fen,
And Saxon Hereward waking, waking,
         Hereward's at it again!

The Cid

1040-1099

*H*AIL to thee, great Castilian don!
Whose valour like bright silver shone!
Whose name struck terror! and whose sword
Spread death among the Moorish horde!
Hail, mighty Cid! whose bold intent
Made thee in life pre-eminent,
And (as my numbers now recount)
Even in death still paramount!

The strangest victory ever read
The Cid achieved when he was dead—
For, in a city hard beset,
Being sick to death, but living yet,
Unto a friend he gave his last
Commands; and when his life had passed
The Spanish followers of the Cid,
Even as he had ordered, did.

Out of his bed they took his corse;
They set it upright on his horse;
They fastened well the saddle, where
It sat with stern and martial air;
About his sword they closed his hand;
His banner, by the breezes fanned,
They raised aloft; and by his side
Five hundred living knights did ride.

And when, from out the city gate,
Upon his horse, erect and straight,
With trumpet blast and rolling drum,
The Cid, embalmed in death did come,
At sight of him, in armour dressed,
His long beard flowing down his breast,
The Moors in all directions fled,
Unwitting that the Cid was dead.

With panting breath and rolling eyes
They raised to heaven frenzied cries
Of 'Allah! Allah! all is vain!
The Cid is on us once again!'
And falling back on every side,
Some gazing on him open-eyed,
While some their sight in terror hid,
'The Cid!' they cried, 'the Cid! the Cid!'

So, cold and stiff and void of breath,
Triumphant on his day of death,
With clang of hoofs and clash of steel,
The Cid was carried to Castille,
And close beside an altar there
They set him on an ivory chair,
Where pilgrims flocked to see his face
For long years staring into space.

Saladin

1137-1193

*H*ERE stands sooty *Sala*din—don't say Sa*lad*in!
His skin is as dark as the Slave of Aladdin!
A sumptuous turban his temples are clad in!
His robe is of silk, which he doesn't look bad in!
And every one knows that the mood he is glad in
Is when he is fighting Crusaders like mad'in
Jerusalem, Jaffa, in Mecca, Bagdad, in
Fact any old city a fight can be had in!

The King of the English would like to have slain him!
The King of the French did his utmost to brain him!
The Emp'ror of Germany tried to obtain him,
Desiring to manacle, shackle and chain him!
Yet none of these monarchs, who failed to restrain him,
Could really dislike or despise or disdain him,
For valour and honour combined to sustain him,
Which made them respect this remarkable Paynim!

And when he desisted from battle's confusions,
His houris refreshed him with fizzy solutions
Of sherbert, and singers made honeyed intrusions,
And conjurers conjured up cunning illusions,
And poets recited rhapsodic effusions,
And dancing-girls twisted in strange revolutions,
While Saladin lay on a cluster of cushions,
In rose-scented water performing ablutions.

Robert Bruce

1306-1329

*W*HEN BRUCE, King of Scotland,
    Was getting the worst
Of the war he was waging
With Edward the First;
When most of his friends
Had been captured or slain,
And the sky over Scotland
Looked very like rain;

When he spent his days hiding
In bushes and trees,
Getting thorns in his fingers
And cuts on his knees;
And when nothing could lighten
The gloom he was feeling—
He lay in a hovel
And stared at the ceiling.

He stared at the ceiling
With thoughts that were black,
Till a spidery spider
Came out of a crack,
A spidery spider
All bulging with thread,
Which she started to spin
In the beam overhead.

She spun the web once,
But the spider-thread broke;
She spun the web twice—
Bruce's interest woke;
She spun the web three times
With pluck unavailing;
She spun the web four times
But still went on failing.

She spun the web five times—
'God bless me!' cried Bruce,
'Yon spidery spider
Must see it's no use!
O spidery spider,
It's plain as a pike
We two are as like as
Two peas are alike!'

She spun the web six times—
'How now!' cried the Scot,
'Don't you know when you're beaten?'
The spider did not,
But calmly proceeded,
As patient as ever,
To start on an obstinate
Seventh endeavour.

She hung and she swung
And she swayed in the air,
While Bruce for the spider
Recited a prayer—
Then he whooped with delight
And sprang up to his feet,
For from one beam to t'other
The web hung complete!

With hope he was filled
And with courage he burned.
'O spider,' he said,
'What a lesson I've learned!
Dear Scotland! of English
Invaders I'll rid it!'
Then Bruce sallied forth
And at Bannockburn did it!

Robin Hood
14th Century

*R*OBIN HOOD
Was an outlawed earl
He took to the wood
With a lovely girl,
And there and then
They were lord and queen
Of a band of men
In Lincoln green—
There was Scarlet Will, and Alan a Dale,
And great big Little John-O,
And Friar Tuck, that fat old buck,
And Much the Miller's son-O!

Robin Hood
He robbed the rich
And gave to the good
And needy, which,
When the moon was bright
And the sport was rare,
Seemed only right
And fair and square
To Scarlet Will, and Alan a Dale,
And great big Little John-O,
and Friar Tuck, that fat old buck,
And Much the Miller's son-O!

Robin Hood
He poached the deer
And moistened his food
With stolen beer—
Hark how they sing
And shout and flout
The knavish king
Who turned him out
With Scarlet Will, and Alan a Dale,
And great big Little John-O,
And Friar Tuck, that fat old buck,
And Much the Miller's son-O!

William Tell
14th Century

*W*ILLIAM TELL
Was a mountaineer,
He yodelled and hunted
And knew no fear,
With bow and arrow
He made no miss,
He loved his son
And they both were Swiss,
With a yodel-oodle-iddle-oo,
Yodel-oodle-ido!

Austrian Gessler
Ruled that part
With a brutal hand
And a ruthless heart,
He stuck up his hat
In the market square
And made the peasants
Salute it there.

William Tell
Wouldn't bow his head,
Austrian Gessler
Scowled and said,
'Your son, you rebel,
I'll execute
Unless you can show me
How well you shoot.

'Behold this apple
So round and red!
This apple I set
On your small boy's head,
And if with an arrow
From yonder tree
You hit this apple,
I'll set him free!'

Tell's brow grew dark
And his eye flashed flame.
At the far-off apple
He took good aim,
He steadied his hand,
His arrow flew—
And *ping!* the apple
Was cleft in two!

Then William Tell
In secret planned
Of the Austrian pest
To rid his land;
He hid in the heights
For many a day
Till Austrian Gessler
Came that way.

Austrian Gessler
Rode below,
Twirling his curly
Mustach-i-o,
And *ping!* an arrow
Like lightning sped,
And Austrian Gessler
Fell down dead!
With a yodel-oodle-iddle-oo,
Yodel-oodle-ido!

Timour the Tartar
1336-1405

*T*IMOUR was a Tartar,
Yellow as an egg!
Yellow was his body
And his face and his leg!
He stamped and he trampled
On the people of the East,
Who fled from Timour
As a Great Wild Beast!
Here comes the Tartar-man!
The terrifying Turk!
Of Siberians and Indians
He Makes Short Work!

Timour was a Tartar,
Yellow as a cake!
He made all his enemies
Shiver and shake!
When he had killed them,
This is what he did,
He piled up their skulls
In a Big Pyramid!
Here comes the Tartar-man!
The terrifying Turk!
Of Armenians and Persians
He Makes Short Work!

Timour was a Tartar,
Yellow as a quince!
Not the sort of hero
We've cared for since!
On his way to China
He came over bad,
And died of distemper,
And Weren't They Glad!
There goes the Tartar-man!
The terrifying Turk!
No one was sorry when
He Knocked Off Work!

Joan of Arc

1412-1431

MAID, what make you
Among your sheep?
Over the meadows,
As in sleep,
I hear the Voices,
Brighter than wine,
Of Margaret, Michael,
Catherine!

Maid, what make you
Of their tale?
Doff your kirtle,
Don your mail,
And save fair France,
Say the divine
Margaret, Michael,
Catherine!

Maid, what make you
At Orleans siege?
I force the English
I free my liege,
I crown my king,
And obey the sign
Of Margaret, Michael,
Catherine!

Maid, what make you
In Rouen Town?
I feel a flame!
I wear a crown!
Father in Heaven,
I see them shine,
Margaret, Michael,
Catherine!

Christopher Columbus
1446-1506

SAID Christopher Columbus,
Before he became renowned,
  'The theory that
  The world is flat
Is certainly most unsound!
  So give me a ship
  To make a trip,
  And west I'll go
  With a yo-heave-ho!
  Straight on I'll steer
  Till I get back here
And prove that the world is round!'

To Christopher Columbus
The King of the Portuguese
  Said 'Fiddle-de-dee!
  You can't fool me
With silly ideas like these!'
  And the King of Spain
  Said, 'Look! it's plain
  The world is far
  From globular—
  Apart from humps
  And lumps and bumps,
It's flat as a piece of cheese!'

When Christopher Columbus
Was feeling as dark as night, ·
  Queen Isabel
  Said, 'Well, well! well!
You possibly may be right!
  So go on a cruise,
  For though your views
  Seem rather cracked,
  And though, in fact,
  I don't expect
  They'll prove correct,
There's always a chance they might!'

Then Christopher Columbus
That mariner so renowned,
  Sailed o'er the sea
  Till one day he
Discovered American ground—
  And therefore all
  Americans call
  The U.S.A.
  Columbia
  In praise of the name
  Of the man who came
To prove that the world was round!

Mary Queen of Scots
1542-1587

*M*ARY, fairest of the fair,
Scotland's queen and England's heir,
By men worshipped to excess,
Was hated by her Cousin Bess.

When a child, she went to France,
And married there with circumstance
The Dauphin, but the Dauphin died
And made a widow of his bride.

Home she came to Scotland's throne,
Where, as dogs about a bone,
Lords and princes vied to bring
Mary her next wedding-ring.

Was she not the Scottish queen?
Might she not in time be seen
Wearing England's golden crown
When Queen Bess had laid it down?

Mary, fairer than the rose,
Next her cousin Darnley chose,
Darnley, weak and discontent,
Treacherous and insolent.

Jealous of her higher place,
Jealous even of her face,
Darnley sought to lay her low
And slew her singer Rizzio.

Darnley died; with Bothwell then
Marriage Mary tried again,
But Bothwell stirred up Scotland's hate
And Mary had to abdicate.

Then she fled in her distress
To England and her Cousin Bess,
Who envied her and, turning pale,
Quickly clapped her into gaol.

A prisoner then for nineteen years,
Bess ignored her pleas and tears,
Till Mary, fairer than the day,
Lost her head at Fotheringay.

So she lived and so she died,
Scotland's pawn and Scotland's pride,
England's bane and England's heir,
Mary, fairest of the fair.

Sir Francis Drake

1550-1596

DEVONSHIRE DRAKE was a sea-dog bold
Who could laugh and swear and swagger and scold!
Young men gaped at the tales he told
  Of the thrills a sea-life offers!
He rounded the world in the *Golden Hind*,
And plundered the wealth of the Western Ind,
So Elizabeth's purse was lined,
  And so he filled her coffers!

> *That is the sort of a man he was,*
> *Sea-dog Sir Francis!*
> *Life is short, so put from port*
> *And take the longest chances!*

There wasn't a ship Sir Francis Drake
Wouldn't undertake to overtake!
He gave the dons a stomach-ache,
  And made their donnas shudder!
Sir Francis Drake he never turned pale!
On a rickety raft he braved the gale
With only a biscuit-bag for a sail
  And a tree-trunk for a rudder!

> *That is the sort of a man he was,*
> *Sea-dog Sir Francis!*
> *Life is short, so put from port*
> *And take the longest chances!*

Devonshire Drake was playing at bowls
When the Spanish Armada neared the shoals,
But all he said was, 'Here she rolls!
  We'll pepper King Philip later!'
Oh, some he fought to the final shot,
And some he sank till he'd settled the lot,
This Protestant, pirate, patriot,
  And very-good-Spaniard-hater!

> *That is the sort of man he was,*
> *Sea-dog Sir Francis!*
> *Life is short, so put from port*
> *And take the longest chances!*

Sir Philip Sidney

1554-1586

*H*ERE blooms the flower
Of Bess's Court,
Whose unstain'd hour
On earth was short.

Of courtesy
He was the prince,
None such as he
Before or since.

He held his cause
In honour's name,
His temper was
A shining flame.

With pen and sword,
In dance and fight,
A lovely lord,
A perfect knight.

On Zutphen's field
By mortal wound
His fate was sealed.
For thirst he swooned.

One ran, and brought
A brimming cup;
But ere he sought
The first sweet sup,

He caught a poor
Man's fevered eye,
Who at death's door
Did near him lie.

Amid the slaughter
Where they bled,
'Take him the water,'
Sidney said—

(The water, sweeter
Then than wine)—
'His need is greater
Yet than mine.'

Crowning his dower
Of high report,
Thus died the flower
Of Bess's Court.

He wrote sweet prose
And sweeter song.
So bright a rose
Could not live long.

Pocahontas

1595-1617

*P*OCAHONTAS
Gentle and wild,
The Indian Chief
Powhatan's child,
In her deerskin-shoes
And her feather-cloak
Lived in Virginia
With her folk.

The red-leaf'd maple,
The pine-tree strong,
The wild-bee's honey,
The oriole's song,
The arrow's whistle,
The victim's yell,
Pocahontas
Knew these things well.

But when the White Men
Sought her land,
These she did not
Understand;
They came like heroes
Of ancient myth,
And when she saw him
She loved John Smith.

The Indian called
The White Man foe,
But Pocahontas
Did not so;
From the tomahawk
And the scalping-knife
Powhatan's daughter
Saved John Smith's life.

For when her idol
Was doomed to die
And bowed his head
As the blade rose high,
Her own brown body
On his she flung
And death was stayed
As the axe-head swung.

And did she wed
The man she saved?
Her story was not
So engraved.
John Rolfe, the settler,
Made her his bride,
And brought her to England,
Where she died.

But Pocahontas
In memory runs
Under Virginia's
Moons and suns,
Swift and eager,
Gentle and wild,
The Indian Chief
Powhatan's child.

The Duke of Marlborough
1650-1722

THE mighty Duke of Marlborough at Blenheim won the day,
And Ramillies and Oudenarde and

> Mal-
> > pla-
> > > quet!

So long as he was fighting, he didn't care a fig,
And he marched into battle in a Great Big Wig!
However fierce the fight, and the fuss however great,
He always kept his

> Wig
> > On
> > > Straight!

The mighty Duke of Marlborough at Blenheim won with ease,
And Oudenarde and Malplaquet and

> Ram-
> > il-
> > > lies!

A hat full of feathers he wore upon his head,
And he changed it for a night-cap when he Went To Bed!
His officers saluted on the field of war,
And his sentinels saluted when they

> Heard
> Him
> > Snore!

The mighty Duke of Marlborough through Blenheim came unscarred,
And Malplaquet and Ramillies and

> Ou-
> > den-
> > > arde!

By day he led his regiments for Good Queen Anne,
And at night he kept his feet warm with a Warming-Pan!
And so he beat his enemies, instead of a retreat,
For he never, never, never, never

> Got
> Cold
> > Feet!

Rob Roy
1671-1734

*R*OB ROY MACGREGOR
Could fling a fine reel,
 Och! aye!
With toe and with heel,
And skirl on the bagpipes
Beyond any man,
And was merry and lawless
And loved by his clan!

Rob Roy Macgregor
Stole cattle and sheep,
 Och! aye!
When folk were asleep,
Driving other men's cows
To his lair from the farm,
With other men's lambkins
Tucked under his arm!

Rob Roy Macgregor
Kept robbing the Roy,
 Och! aye!
With Jacobite joy!
He helped all his friends,
And he cursed all his foes,
Crying, 'Down with the King
And the Duke of Montrose!'

Rob Roy Macgregor
Was partial to loot,
 Och! aye!
And a rebel to boot!
His heart it was good,
If the ways they were bad,
Of Rob Roy Macgregor
That daredevil lad!

Flora Macdonald

1722-1790

*O*H, raw the nicht and keen the blast,
    And lowly was the shed
Whaur Charlie lay aboon the brae,
    A price upon his head.
'Twas Flo Macdonald tae him there,
    Amid the mire an' murk,
The garments bore her handmaid wore,
    Her bonnie Betty Burke.

'Put on this flowered gown, my king,
    And quilted petticoat,
And you and I will sail to Skye
    All in an open boat.'

'Beneath yon camlet cloak, my dear,
    I'll hide my kilt an' dirk,
And gang wi' ye across the sea
    As bonnie Betty Burke.'

'The wind is up at sea, my king,
    The hunt is up on shore!
Till you stand sound on friendly ground
    I'll leave ye nevermore!'

'Then on the heathery heights, my dear,
    Nae mair I'll crouch an' lurk,
But tak my way by light o' day
    As bonnie Betty Burke.'

'There's danger on the sea, my king,
    There's death upon the strand,
But I will brave wi' you the wave
    And save you either hand.'

'Now let you gae to sleep, my dear,
    Your dreams nae ill shall irk,
For wha will keep ye in your sleep
    But bonnie Betty Burke?'

They twa hae crossed the angry sea,
    They twa hae come tae Skye,
And handsome Flo wi' pride aglow
    Has kissed her king good-bye.
'Farewell, my Flo, farewell, my dear,
    I'll mind for aye this work!'
'Farewell, farewell to bonnie Charles,
    And bonnie Betty Burke!'

George Washington

1732-1799

WHEN little George was quite a child
    He found a little hatchet,
And chopped with glee a cherry-tree
    In order to dispatch it.
He chopped it up, he chopped it down,
He raised the axe and dealt it whacks,
And when it fell, he knew quite well
    That somebody would catch it!

Then George's father came along
    And said in tones decided:
'It seems to me this cherry-tree
    Looks shockingly lop-sided!
Who chopped it up? Who chopped it down?'
His voice was shrill—it boded ill!
And George turned red but frankly said:
    'I cannot lie, dad, I did!'

And did the father take a birch
    To beat the trembling sinner?
Or say, 'You see that cherry-tree—
    Well, there you see your dinner!'
No, no! he looked George up and down,
And cried, 'Good youth! you've told the truth!
Bravo, my lad! your happy dad
    Has clearly bred a winner!'

No truer word was ever spoke!
    Arrived at manhood's station,
Even as he had whacked the tree,
    George whacked the English nation!
He marched his army up and down,
He freed his land from England's hand,
For which his name and fame became
    Columbia's inspiration!

So once a year the U.S.A.
    Does honour to the chopper
Who made with glee that cherry-tree
    And England come a cropper.
With rockets up and crackers down
In every State they celebrate
George Washington, the upright son
    Who would not tell a whopper!

Nelson
1758-1805

NELSON only had one eye —
    What! just the one eye?
  Yes, just the one eye,
But the Froggies agreed it was much too spry
  When he fought for his King and his Country!
And he won the Battle of Trafalgár,
Which shows one eye can see as far
As two can see, or even three,
  When you fight for your King and your Country!

Nelson only had one arm—
    What! just the one arm?
  Yes, just the one arm,
But the Froggies agreed it worked like a charm
  When he fought for his King and his Country!
For he won the Battle of Trafalgár,
Which shows one arm is as good in a spar
As two can be, or even three,
  When you fight for your King and your Country!

Nelson he was sick at sea—
    What! seasick at sea?
  Yes, seasick at sea,
But he brought up his guns as well as his tea
  When he fought for his King and his Country!
And he won the Battle of Trafalgár,
Which shows that sickness is no bar
To a victoree, or two or three,
  When you fight for your King and your Country!

Napoleon
1769-1821

*N*APOLEON, when the day is done,
  On Saint Helena stands,
And gazes at the setting sun,
  And dreams of distant lands
Where once the rulers feared his glance
  When from the ranks he rose
To be the Emperor of France
  And trample on her foes—
But now, encircled by the sea,
A solitary exile he.

He sees again with brooding eyes
  His Corsica in flower,
He hears the Revolution rise
  That lifted him to power,
He sees again the laurel wreath
  He won in many a war,
He hears France cry with eager breath,
  'Long live the Emperor!'—
While now, encircled by the sea,
A solitary exile he.

He sees the chain of fire that spells
  In Moscow his defeat,
He hears again the Kremlin's bells
  And tramp of marching feet,
He sees the shadow on his reign
  As Europe's tempests brew,
He hears, oh fateful toll! again
  The guns of Waterloo—
And now, encircled by the sea,
A solitary exile he.

Napoleon, as the daylight fades,
  His arm across his breast,
Watches the scarlet cavalcades
  Of sunset in the west.
Oh, are not these his Grenadiers
  Arisen from the grave?
And is this booming in his ears
  Only the breaking wave?—
Night falls.   Encircled by the sea,
A solitary exile he.

Wellington
1769-1852

*T*HIS here's the Iron Dook
    For whom the drum goes bang!
And them as don't approve of him
    May all of 'em go hang!
In Eighteen Hunderd *and* Fifteen
    He got up on his pony,
And went with his drum to Bel-gi-um
    To rid the world of Boney!

This here's the Iron Dook
    For whom the fife goes tweet!
And them as can't abide his ways
    Are them he'd like to meet!
In Eighteen Hunderd *and* Fifteen,
    With Bloocher for his crony,
He went with fife-and-drum to Bel-gi-um
    To make short work of Boney!

This here's the Iron Dook
    For whom the cornet toots!
He won his spurs at Waterloo,
    And left the world his boots!
In Eighteen Hunderd *and* Fifteen,
    Like mince for a polony,
With cornet-fife-and-drum he went to Bel-gi-um
    And made mincemeat of Boney!

Lady Hester Stanhope
1778-1839

*O*N the low hills of Lebanon,
Far from her native Somerset,
The Lady Hester Stanhope dwelt
Behind a grey stone parapet.

Pitt's niece and Chatham's grand-daughter,
This fiery heir of famous names
For forty years, among her kind,
Lived the calm life of English dames.

Sudden, when half her years were spent,
Departing from her native place,
To Smyrna and Jerusalem
The English lady turned her face.

Fearless she crossed the desert plains,
Fearless she faced the desert hordes;
Because she scorned all hurt and harm
She queened it over Arab lords.

When the ferocious Bedouin rode,
With pointed spear, this woman gaunt
Rose in her stirrups, raised her veil,
And cried in hollow tones, *'Avaunt!'*

And ever grew her fame and power,
And ever grew the murmurous
Whisper among the Arab tribes:
'A Prophetess is come to us!'

Not far from Sidon's ancient pile,
This Prophetess, this Desert Queen,
In a neglected convent dwelt
Communing with the Great Unseen.

No books she read but in the stars,
Nor tasted any food but milk;
Her eyes glowed in her milk-white face
Neath turban-folds of pallid silk.

Black slaves and Arabs served her needs
In her dilapidated halls,
Waiting to rob her of her goods
When death should steal within her walls.

When travellers came from the West,
Whose mothers knew her as a child,
Gracious among her veils she rose
With welcoming words and glances wild.

She asked for news of Somerset—
But swiftly passed to vaster spheres—
Muttered of demons and black arts,
And whispered, *'The Messiah nears!'*

Believed and served, revered and feared,
She died. Now through the chambers fly
The pillaging and plundering slaves,
Like jackals when the moon is high.

On the low hills of Lebanon,
Far from the vales of Somerset,
The Lady Hester Stanhope sleeps
Behind her grey stone parapet.

Garibaldi

1807-1882

GARIBALDI tilled the soil,
And grew the olives that give the oil,
And sowed the seed that bears the vine
That yields the grapes that make the wine.

But while he slashed the weeds and wrought
To clear his little patch, he thought
How everywhere his native land
Was choked with weeds of foreign brand.

He thought how lovely Venice lay
A captive under Austrian sway;
How Sicily and Naples groaned
Under the Frenchman there enthroned;

How Italy's unhappy king
Even in Rome played second string—
So Garibaldi left his farm
And called on Italy to arm.

All Italy enkindled when
He raised his Thousand Redshirt Men!
Twas Redshirts here and Redshirts there,
Italian Redshirts everywhere!

A brave new soul awakened in
The land from Naples to Turin;
Wherever Garibaldi came,
The Redshirts followed like a flame.

He liberated Sicily,
From Naples made the Frenchman flee,
Nor rested till his king sat down
Neath Italy's united crown.

They offered him for his reward
A castle suited to a lord,
Promised his son a place of power,
His daughter, a princess's dower.

But Garibaldi, void of greed,
Took nothing but a bag of seed,
Called on his Redshirts to disarm,
And went back to his country farm—

Went back again to till the soil,
And grow the olives that give the oil,
And sow the seed that bears the vine
That yields the grapes that make the wine.

David Livingstone
1813-1873

*O*H, have you heard of Livingstone,
Dr. David Livingstone,
Who went to Darkest Africa and solved her darkest riddle?
We knew that she had edges
As we know a field has hedges,
But Livingstone discovered that she also had a middle.
Then sing aloud in chorus, with a tom-tom playing solo,
Cabango and Kabompo and Ilala and Dilolo,
Shapanga and Katanga and Ujiji and Chambese,
Not forgetting Bangweolo and Nyasa and Zambesi!

Oh, where is Dr. Livingstone,
Dr. David Livingstone,
Who went away to Africa to tread the track unbeaten?
We haven't had a letter
For so long, perhaps we'd better
Send Mr. H. M. Stanley, just to see if he's been eaten.
Come, sing again in chorus, though I know it isn't easy,
Cabango and Kabompo and Nyasa and Zambesi,
Ilala and Dilolo and Ujiji and Shapanga,
Not forgetting Bangweolo and Chambese and Katanga!

'Good morning, Dr. Livingstone!
Delighted, Dr. Livingstone,
To find you safe and sound in this environment forsaken!'
'Good morning. Mr. Stanley!
Your behaviour has been manly,
I'm very glad to see you — will you have some eggs and bacon?
And sing with me in chorus, while the natives do a romp-O,
Nyasa and Zambesi and Cabango and Kabompo,
Chambese and Ujiji and Ilala and Dilolo,
Shapanga and Katanga, not forgetting Bangweolo!'

Grace Darling
1815-1842

GRACE DARLING, the Pride of the Lifeboat,
   Was a lass of Northumbrian stock;
She knew from a child a coast that was wild
   And breakers that battered the rock;
Her father, one William D. Darling,
   Kept the lighthouse on Longstone, in Farne,
While Grace in her home by the spray and the foam
   The holes in his stockings would darn.

'Twas in Thirty-Eight that a tempest
   Blew up amid lightning and rain,
And far out at sea, bound from Hull to Dundee,
   The *Forfarshire* signalled in vain!
'Oh, who,' exclaimed William D. Darling,
   'Our lifeboat to launch will dare try?'
Then his brave daughter Grace looked at him straight in the face
   And said, 'You, my dear father, and I.'

Unaided, they launched it together!
   Unaided, they fought with the tide!
But, high though it ran, Grace pulled like a man,
   With Courage and Faith by her side!
And the bosom of William D. Darling
   Swelled with pride of the child he had bred,
For she stuck to her oar 'mid the din and the roar
   Of the thunder that rolled overhead!

At last they arrived at the vessel!
   The breakers were flooding the deck,
But, though wet to the skin, Grace never gave in,
   And rescued nine souls from the wreck.
And the daughter of William D. Darling
   Was toasted from Falmouth to Farne,
While, meek as a mouse, she went back to the house,
   Her dear father's stockings to darn.

Florence Nightingale
1820-1910

*W*HEN cannon-roar and musket-rattle
    Shook the Crimea far and wide,
Many fell dead in bloody battle,
    But more for lack of nursing died;
Uncared, uncomforted, uncherished,
    Moaning, the sick and wounded lay,
Till, to the plague-spot where they perished,
    A lady came from far away.

With courage high, across the water
    She came in answer to their call;
Even in the heart of daily slaughter
    She raised her healing hospital.
She faced the ague and the fever,
    Filth and fatigue and bitter chill;
Ever she named her will, and ever
    England compelled to grant her will.

Constant and staunch, however tested,
    Bravely she faced the long campaign;
She worked, she nursed, she never rested,
    Soothing the soldiers in their pain.
Often at night, the sick men turning
    To ease their hot and heavy heads,
Would see her, with her dim lamp burning,
    Silently walk between their beds.

Her name through every English city
    Rang louder than the Russian gun—
The name this lady's care and pity
    From the dry lips of soldiers won:
For when, her vigil still unended,
    She cooled their brows with fever damp,
The men she nightly watched and tended
    Named her the Lady of the Lamp.

Buffalo Bill
1846-1917

I SAY! What a thrill!
Here's Buffalo Bill,
The King of the Cowboys in valour and skill,
With his fringes of leather, his cowpuncher's hat,
His lasso and pistols and boots and all that!
    Stout-hearted and hairy,
    With confidence airy
He slew the wild buffalo roaming the prairie,
And played the chief part in exciting events
Enacted around the Red Indian tents,
    And when the news came,
    As part of the game,
That the Redskins had set his log-cabin aflame,
    He rode without pause
    To put down the cause
'Mid the yelling of braves and the squawking of squaws.
    He fought a lot more
    As Scoutmaster for
The troops of the North in the Great Civil War,
And America's mail through the land was conveyed
By his Pony Express ere the railway was made.
    And I say! what a thrill
    When Buffalo Bill,
Who, agog for adventure, could never keep still,
Got up a fine circus, to show every one
How the Redskin-and-buffalo business was done!
    What glee and what glory
    To see his life-story
Presented in episodes pleasantly gory,
With whips and with scalps that were cracked with a will
By breakneck, unbeatable Buffalo Bill!

Emmeline Pankhurst
1858-1928

*M*ILITANT, vigorous,
    Rampant and rigorous,
Emmeline Pankhurst cried, 'Britain! take note!
    Vote, Votes for Women! I
    Won't rest, by Jiminy,
Till, like my husband, I'm given a Vote!
    Are men superior?
    Women inferior?
Suffragettes, come! pass your days and your nights
    Hatching up critical
    Crises political,
Fearlessly planned to procure us our Rights!'

    Then with her following,
    Hooting and hollowing,
Emmeline shouted when Ministers spoke;
    Windows they battered in;
    Acid they scattered in
Pillar-posts, setting the letters a-smoke;
    Next, from the putting-green
    They started cutting green
Pieces of turf twice as big as your hand—
    Thus her tenacity,
    Backed by audacity,
Made Mrs. Pankhurst the scorn of the land.

    Statesmen detested her,
    Policemen arrested her,
Colonels in clubs became pink at her name,
    Newspapers sneered at her,
    Little boys jeered at her,
Still Mrs. Pankhurst went on with the game,
    Till her ability
    Vanquished hostility—
Now women vote, for a vote they have got—
    And since her victory,
    No contradictory
Candidate dares to suggest they should not!

Nansen
1861-1930

*T*HIS is the saga of Nansen, pioneer of the North,
The saga of Fridtjof Nansen and the *Fram* that bore him forth.

Tall was he as a viking, kindly and strong was he,
The blood of his roving fathers drove him from sea to sea.

Blue were the eyes of Nansen, keener than ice or fire,
Fixed as the star they gazed on, the Pole Star of his desire.

Better than fields of flowers the ice-fields Nansen loved,
Where man's endurance was tested, and his faith in God was proved.

Better than grass in the valleys he loved the snow on the heights,
Where the fierce white Arctic called him, flashing her northern lights.

Steering the *Fram* to the ice-pack that ever did northward shift,
He let her drift with the ice-floe as far as the floe would drift.

When the *Fram* could fare no farther, locked in the icy jam,
With his dogs, his sleds and his snowshoes, Nansen quitted the *Fram*.

The white whale blew in the channel, the white bear prowled the snows,
Like fiery quartz the drift-ice glowed in the sunset's rose.

The walrus barked in the waters, the great auk skimmed the ice,
The Aurora Borealis turned heaven to paradise.

The leaping fox, the crested seal, scampered and hid from sight,
Three white fountains of moonlight sprang on the deep blue night.

Three years, three years absent, his fate three years unknown,
The rover under the Pole Star was lost in the frozen zone.

Three years, three years wandering under the blind white spell,
Home he came to Norway with a marvellous tale to tell.

The saga of Fridtjof Nansen, who, questing the Pole, went forth,
And left the *Fram* abandoned to silence in the North.